QUIZ THE SEASON

THE BOOK OF CHRISTMAS TRIVIA

QUIZ THE SEASON

THE BOOK OF CHRISTMAS TRIVIA

HEATHER REVESZ

BARNES
& NOBLE
BOOKS

NEW YORK

The author wishes to thank everyone who provided help and encouragement: Rick Campbell, Sharon Bosley, Sallye Leventhal, the Russell Family, and the Revesz Family.

For Joe.

ISBN: 0-7607-3277-9

Text design by Maureen Slattery

Printed in China

04 05 MP 9 8 7 6 5 4 3 2

Traditions & Customs

According to American tradition, what color is Santa Claus's suit?

> Red.

How do many children in America believe that Santa enters their houses?

> Down the chimney.

What Saint's feast day is celebrated on December 6?

> Saint Nicholas. Although Pope Paul VI ordered this feast day dropped from the official Roman Catholic calendar in 1969, many people in Europe still celebrate this day.

Who was Saint Nicholas?

> A monk named Hagios Nikolaos (270–310), the Bishop of Myra (present-day Turkey).

Where does the name Santa Claus come from?

It started with good old Saint Nicholas. The real Saint Nicholas was celebrated all over Europe as a symbol of generosity, and his feast day became a day to exchange gifts. Soon, children believed this benevolent Saint brought them gifts on his feast day. Saint Nicholas is Sinter Klaas in Dutch—when Dutch settlers came to America they brought the legend of the gift-bearing Sinter Klaas, which, when pronounced by Americans, became Santa Claus.

Saint Nicholas has been the patron saint of which of the following: children, sailors, prisoners, bakers, pawnbrokers, wolves, Russia?

All of them.

What nickname for Santa Claus did the German phrase CHRIST KINDLEIN *(Christ child) become?*

> *"Kriss Kringle." Nineteenth century Europeans told the legend of a Christ kindlein who brought gifts. Later it became synonymous with the famous gift-giving Santa Claus, who as we all know by now came from the legends of the generous Saint Nicholas!*

What as Saint Nicholas usually pictured wearing until the early 1800s

> *The red robe and tall pointed hat of the European Bishop.*

What country issued the first official Christmas stamp?

> *Canada, in 1898.*

What organization first dressed men up in Santa Claus suits to solicit donations?

> *The Salvation Army, in the 1890s, raised money to pay for the free Christmas meals they provided to needy families.*

What soft-drink company started using the image of a jolly round Santa Claus in their advertising in the 1930s?

> *Coca-Cola®.*

What Midwestern state has a town called Santa Claus?

> *Indiana.*

Where did the tradition of hanging stockings originate?

This tradition involves good old Saint Nicholas as well. According to legend, a poor man could not afford any dowries for his three daughters. One morning the family awoke to find a bag of gold in one of the stockings that had been hung on the chimney to dry. Saint Nicholas had anonymously donated the gold, and threw it down the chimney, where it accidentally landed in a stocking. On the next two nights the same thing happened. From this legend, children began hanging stockings for Saint Nicholas to bring them presents.

Originated in the 1950s and '60s, what were the bank accounts that helped you save for Christmas presents called?

> *Christmas Clubs. Many believe the advent of credit cards helped with the decline of this savings method.*

Why are evergreens brought into homes during Christmas time?

> *Pre-Christians used the evergreen tree as a symbol of fertility, and the branches, as well as the trees themselves were used in winter solstice celebrations. Christians began incorporating these customs into the celebration of the birth of Jesus. These festivities also included the preparation of special foods, singing, and gift-giving.*

What country is credited with starting the Christmas tree decorating tradition as we know it?

> *Germany, in the 16th century. Many historians believe early Mystery plays performed on December 24 for Adam and Eve's feast day used a decorated evergreen tree as symbol of the Tree of Life in Eden (called Paradis Baum). The tree was decorated with apples. Soon people began bringing their own "Paradise Tree" into their homes, and decorating it with food.*

Who were the first in America to decorate their homes with fir trees?

> *German settlers in Pennsylvania in the 1800s.*

What British royal helped popularize the use of Christmas trees in both England and America?

Queen Victoria; her German husband Prince Albert brought the Christmas tree tradition with him to England. A sketch of the royal family in front of a Christmas tree in 1846 made the practice immediately fashionable.

What Protestant reformer is rumored to have started the tradition of decorating Christmas trees with candles?

Martin Luther. Legend has it that Luther was walking home through a forest of fir trees, brought one home for his children and decorated it with candles to represent the beauty of the stars shining down.

What invention in the late 1800s helped popularize the Christmas tree decorating tradition?

The invention of electric lights for Christmas trees. They replaced the dangerous candles that often caused fires in homes.

Who invented the first electric Christmas tree lights?

> *There are several stories surrounding the creation of these holiday favorites, but the most common theory is that Edward Johnson, a colleague of Thomas Edison, created a string of small electric bulbs in 1882 and used them to decorate his Christmas tree. The strand consisted of about 80 red, white, and blue bulbs. General Electric began making Christmas tree lights for sale in 1890, but they were cost prohibitive (to light a tree at this time would cost about $2,000 today). By 1920 Christmas lights were being machine-made, making them an affordable holiday custom.*

Which Christmas trees are known to last the longest?

> *Firs and Scotch pine.*

What is the most popular type of Christmas tree in the United States?

> Scotch pine, mostly because the needles tend not to drop off after the tree becomes dry.

Which Christmas trees are known to be the most fragrant?

> Firs, including Douglas, white, and grand.

Approximately how many Christmas trees are sold in the United States each year?
a) 25 million
b) 36 million
c) 46 million

> b. About 36 million.

About how many U.S. families prefer artificial trees?
a) 25 million
b) 36 million
c) 46 million

c. 46 million.

What tasty movie treat is often strung on wire and hung on Christmas trees?

Popcorn.

What do stars placed atop Christmas trees represent?

The Star of Bethlehem that led the three wise men to Jesus.

*What is the best way to photograph
a lit Christmas tree?*
a) Use a tripod
b) Use fast film
c) Turn off surrounding lights
d) Tturn on overhead lights

> *a, b, and c.*

*What did Carl Otis invent in the
1940s that became fashionable tree
decorations in the 1950s and 1960s?*

> *"Bubble lights" for Christmas trees. These "retro"
> decorations have recently made a comeback and
> are available once again in stores.*

*What do you call the piece of fabric that circles the
bottom of a Christmas tree?*

> *A skirt.*

What startling fact regarding Christmas trees happened for the first time in 1991?

Artificial trees outsold real ones.

In 2001, what video game system was considered a runaway hit for the Christmas gift-giving season?

Sony's Playstation 2.

What movie based on a best-selling children's book produced some of the best selling toys in 2001?

HARRY POTTER AND THE SORCERER'S STONE.

**A Christmas fad in 1988 was a toy ball
that looked like a rubber porcupine.
What was it called?**

> *Koosh ball.*

**What toy can sometimes be found
circling the bottom of a Christmas
tree?**

> *A train.*

**What lifelike baby orphan dolls
begged to be adopted by children
during the 1983 holiday season?**

> *Cabbage-Patch Kids®. Parents camped out
> overnight in front of toy stores in hopes of
> grabbing one of these popular dolls.*

What orange must-have doll was auctioned off at E-bay for sometimes triple its retail price during Christmas 1996?

> *Tickle-me-Elmo®.*

What easy to care for "pet" was a popular gift in 1975?

> *Pet rock.*

What 1998 toy craze was helped along by mentions from Rosie O'Donnell?

> *Furby.*

1993 saw the beginnings of this collectable toy craze, whose "original nine" included Legs the Frog, Patti the Platypus, and Flash the Dolphin.

> *Beanie Babies®. By 1998, Ty, Inc. sales, the creator of the plush collectables, exceeded one billion dollars.*

Under what sun sign of the zodiac are those born on December 25?

> *Capricorn.*

What top-selling board game, based on trivial knowledge, hit the U.S. in 1993?

> *Trivial Pursuit®. Within a year 20 million games were sold in the U.S. alone.*

What is the astrological symbol for December 25 birthdays?

> The ram.

When did George Washington's famous crossing of the Delaware take place?

> December 25, 1776.

Name the famous town in Virginia that shows visitors what is was like to celebrate Christmas in the 1770s.

> Williamsburg.

Ornaments made from limes, lemons, or oranges covered with whole cloves are called what?

> Pomander balls.

What flower is known as the "Christmas lily"?

Amaryllis.

Why is Schlumbergera truncata also known as the "Christmas cactus"?

Its flowers resemble red bells that bloom in December.

What are KUGELS?

Popular in the 1850s, these ornaments were lead-lined glass balls filled with colored wax.

What contribution did Max Eckhardt make involving Christmas decorations?

This German ornament maker convinced Corning Glass in the 1940s to machine manufacture ornaments, making them widely available and inexpensive to Americans.

What cone-shaped ornaments did the Victorians fill with dried herbs or candies?

Cornucopias.

The first of these, issued in 1907, was to help "Stamp Out Tuberculosis." What were they?

Christmas Seals. The first seals were offered for 25 for one penny. The "seals" raised $3,000 that first Christmas season, and helped spread the word that the "White Plague" could be beaten.

What is the Hawaiian Christmas greeting?

Mele Kalikimaka, which was also the title of a popular song in the 1950s, sung by Bing Crosby.

What are small gifts purchased to place in stockings usually called?

> Stocking stuffers.

What color are Christmas M&M's?

> Red and green.

What Christmas-related name do towns in Maryland, Pennsylvania, Georgia, Connecticut, and Kentucky share?

> Bethlehem.

What are the calendars that count down the days until Christmas called?

> Advent calendars. Each day has a small door that is opened to reveal pictures, verses, candy, and sometimes small presents.

In what century did Christians start celebrating the birthday of Jesus?

The fourth century.

What was this birthday celebration first called (hint: it's not "Christmas!")?

The Feast of the Nativity.

Why is Christmas celebrated on December 25?

Since no one is sure of the exact date of Christ's birth, Pope Julius I (on or about 350 A.D.) chose this date in an effort to replace the non-Christian wintertime festivals, primarily those of Saturnus and Mithras.

What Saint is credited for assembling the first nativity scene in 1223 in order to demonstrate the birth of Christ?

> *Saint Frances of Assisi.*

What is a manger?

> *A trough where livestock feed.*

Why was Jesus born in a manger?

> *According to Luke, because there was no room at the inn when Mary and Joseph arrived in Bethlehem. "And she brought forth her firstborn son, and wrapped him in swaddling clothes, and laid him in a manger; because there was no room for them in the inn." (Luke 2:7.)*

The Old English phrase CHRISTES MAESSE is the origin of what modern English word?

Christmas. The phrase means "Festival of Christ," and entered our vernacular around 1050.

According to Orthodox tradition, what are the names of the three wise men?

Gaspar, Melchior, Balthazar. They saw the Star of Bethlehem and traveled from the East in order to worship the baby Jesus.

Where is Bethlehem?

In the Middle East, on the West Bank, about five miles south of Jerusalem.

When is Christmas celebrated in Bethlehem?

Those following the Gregorian calendar celebrate on December 25; according to the Julian calendar it's on January 6; and those that go by the Armenian calendar celebrate on January 19.

Comets, supernova, and planetary alignment are all theories that have all been offered by astronomers to explain what phenomenon?

The Star of Bethlehem.

What gifts did the wise men bring the baby Jesus?

Gold, frankincense, and myrrh.

What the heck is myrrh?

> *Myrrh, and frankincense for that matter, are oil-based incenses. They were often used for barter in the time of Christ.*

Midnight mass was introduced by the Roman Catholic Church in what century?

> *The fifth century.*

What are the wise men called in the Bible?

> *Magi. Tradition states that there were three, but the Bible doesn't actually specify how many there were. Three was a guess based on the number of gifts brought to the baby Jesus.*

According to Luke, when the angel of the Lord came to the shepherds in the field to tell them about the birth of Jesus, how did they first react?

> *"They were sore afraid."*

What does "advent" mean?

> *"Coming"; to Christians it means the coming or birth of Jesus on Christmas day.*

When does Advent start?

> *Advent starts on the fourth Sunday before Christmas, and ends on Christmas Eve at sundown.*

What comprises an Advent Wreath?

> The Advent Wreath, usually a circle of evergreens, holds four candles, each of which is lit to celebrate successive Sundays in the Church season. Three of the candles are purple (the liturgical color of Advent); the fourth is pink and is reserved for lighting on the third Sunday. A white candle—the Christ candle—can be placed at the center of the wreath and is to be lit on Christmas Eve.

What is a creche?

> A nativity scene.

What does a census have to do with Jesus's birth?

> Joseph and Mary were traveling to Bethlehem on the orders of Caesar Augustus, who was taking a census for tax reasons. Joseph was originally from Bethlehem.

Where were Mary and Joseph traveling from?

>Nazareth.

What celebration was outlawed in Boston from 1659 to 1681?

>Christmas. The Puritans believed Christmas contained too many festive pagan practices, not to mention the Catholic overtones.

When is the Epiphany celebrated?

>January 6. It is also called Twelfth Night.

What is the Epiphany?

>In Eastern churches, Epiphany celebrates the baptism of Jesus; in Western churches, it celebrates the giving of gifts from the wise men to Jesus.

What two books in the New Testament describe Jesus's birth?

> Matthew (1:18–2:12) and Luke (1:12–1:56).

What is the name of the angel that told Mary she would be giving birth to the son of God?

> Gabriel.

What are "swaddling clothes"?

> Long pieces of cloth that were used to wrap up babies tightly at the time of Jesus's birth.

Until WWI, the German town of Luscha supplied almost all of what Christmas decoration?

> Blown-glass ornaments for trees.

*Used as a tree decoration, what was
tinsel first made of?*

> Real silver. It was made in Germany in the 1600s.
> The silver was pulled into thin strips to place on
> Christmas trees.

*Where does the custom of hanging
wreaths come from?*

> Probably from ancient Rome, where it was used as
> a symbol of victory and celebration.

*Coinciding with the start of the penny
post in England, what is Sir Henry
Cole credited with sending the first of?*

> Sir Henry sent the first commercially produced
> Christmas card in 1843. John Calcott Horsely was
> the artist who designed the card that featured a
> drawing of a family Christmas dinner, with two
> side panels of illustrations of Christmas charity.

How did Louis Prang help a certain Christmas custom develop in America?

In the 1870s Prang began producing the first American commercial Christmas Cards. His cards featured mostly flowers and birds.

What were very popular images on Christmas cards in England in the 1880s?

Dead robins. Historians have yet to come up with a feasible explanation for this craze.

When did giant balloons first make their way into Macys's Thanksgiving Day Parade, which many consider the kick-off to the holidays?

1927. They were a dachshund, a dinosaur, and a bunch of turkeys.

What friendly Christmas custom stemmed from an ancient Celtic symbol of fertility?

Decorating with mistletoe. Mistletoe was revered by the Celts as a special plant. In fact mistletoe was banned by the Christian church for years because of its pagan associations. It was the Victorians who revived its use as decoration at Christmastime, and began the "kissing" custom as well. A berry from the plant was plucked for each kiss exchanged under it. When the berries were gone, the kissing stopped.

What country does the poinsettia come from?

Mexico. It is the leafy blooms on these plants that create the beautiful colors.

Who introduced the poinsettia to the United States?

> In 1828, Dr. Joel Poinsett, American Ambassador to Mexico, brought the plant back from Mexico, where it was thought to resemble the Star of Bethlehem.

What is the Oklahoma state flower?

> Mistletoe.

What were the first two states to make Christmas an official holiday?

> Louisiana and Arkansas in 1831.

When did Christmas become an official holiday in the U.S.?

> It was signed into law on June 26, 1870, under President Grant.

What president first brought a Christmas tree to the White House?

> *Franklin Pierce, in 1856. He was a New Hampshire native, where decorating trees had become a tradition.*

What president first had electric lights on the White House Christmas tree?

> *Grover Cleveland in 1895.*

What president made Thanksgiving a week earlier to help retailers at Christmas?

> *FDR. Before the Depression, Thanksgiving was held on the last Thursday in November.*

What was General Sherman's Christmas gift to President Lincoln in 1864?

> The city of Savannah, which he took on December 21, 1864.

When did the tradition of decorating the "national" Christmas tree on the White House lawn begin?

> In 1923 under President Calvin Coolidge. The tree came from a forest in Vermont.

Why was only the top of the national Christmas tree lit in 1979, instead of the entire tree?

> President Jimmy Carter broke the tradition, in order to honor the Iranian hostages.

According to the poem "The Night Before Christmas," what are the names of Santa's reindeer?

> Dasher, Dancer, Prancer, Vixen, Comet, Cupid, Donder (or Donner, there is some controversy here), and Blitzen. Rudolph wasn't introduced until the 1940s.

Who is Santa's only female sleigh-pulling reindeer?

> Vixen.

Where is Christmas Island?

> There are two: One in Micronesia in the Pacific; one in the Indian Ocean. Both were "discovered" by Europeans at Christmastime, hence the name.

What country controls the Christmas Islands, found in the Indian Ocean?

> Australia.

What do Humphrey Bogart, Sir Isaac Newton, Anwar Sadat, Jimmy Buffet, and Sissy Spacek have in common?

> They were all born on December 25.

How many years has New York City's Rockefeller Center had a Christmas tree?

> In 1931, construction workers put up the first tree on the building site. 1933 was the date of the first formal tree lighting ceremony.

CHRISTMAS
AROUND THE WORLD

In Italy, what is a PRESPIO?

> A manger scene, usually set up nine days before
> Christmas.

How about NACIMIENTOS, from Spain?

> Also a nativity scene.

What is Christmas Eve called in Spain?

> **LA NOCHE BUENA,** or "The Blessed Night."

**What feast kicks off the Christmas
season in Spain?**

> The Feast of the Immaculate Conception, starting
> on December 8.

In Germany, many bakeries feature Christmas scenes in windows made out of what edible confection?

Marzipan.

Some Germans believe that Christmas Eve is a magical night on which animals can do what?

Speak.

What do the French call carols?

Noëls.

What does the lucky person who finds the prize inside of the galette, a French pastry made for the feast of Epiphany, get?

They get to be King or Queen for the day.

What are the Mexican Christmas lanterns called FAROLITOS *made of?*

> Brown paper bags cut intricately with various designs.

Match the traditional Christmas tree decoration with the proper country.

1) Poland   a) brightly painted
2) Sweden   wooden ornaments
3) Lithuania   b) spider and a web
4) Czechoslovakia c) decorations featuring
5) Ukraine   peacocks and other birds
                   d) painted eggshells
                   e) straw birdcages

1 – c; 2 – a; 3 – e; 4 – d; 5 – b.

In Sweden, what pulls Santa's sleigh?

Goats.

In Sweden, who gets to dress up as the "Queen of Light" for St. Lucia's Day?

The eldest daughter of the family.

When is the final celebration of the Christmas season held in Sweden?

St. Knut's Day, January 13. Decorations are taken down, and the children are allowed to eat the last of the candies that adorned the Christmas tree.

In Holland, St. Nicholas Eve is celebrated with a LETTERBANKET. What kind of cake is this?

A "letter cake" made into the shape of the first letter of the family's last name.

Do Australian's have white Christmases?

No, December is summertime in Australia.

When is the traditional gift-giving day in Italy?

January 6, Epiphany.

What glows in the windows of many Irish homes on Christmas Eve?

Candles.

In England, when is "Stir Up Sunday"?

The Sunday before Advent. Traditionally, it was the last occasion where cakes and puddings could be made in time for Christmas Eve.

In Germany, Nurnberg
CHRISTKINDLESMARKT is the oldest
remaining what?

> Christmas fair. It has been held for over 400
> years.

At Christmastime in Sweden, what are
some homes decorated with, in order
to remind them that Jesus was born in
a manger?

> Straw.

What do children in Mexico leave under
the tree on the night of January 5 for
the Three Kings to fill with presents?

> Their shoes.

Who is Father Christmas?

When Oliver Cromwell stopped Christmas celebrations in England in the mid-1600s, and forbade the mention of Saint Nicholas, mummers began acting in plays starring "Father Christmas," based on many pre-Christian legends.

What is the day after Christmas called in England?

Boxing Day, or Saint Stephen's Day. The most common theory on how this holiday was named refers to the opening of alms boxes for the poor on this day.

The POSADA in Mexico reenacts what?

The search by Mary and Joseph to find lodging in Bethlehem. Mexican children dress up and walk from house to house, asking if there is any room at the inn.

*In Poland and the Czech Republic, a
place is left empty at the dinner table
on Christmas Eve for whom?*

> Christ.

In Poland, an OPLATEK *(a kind of a
biscuit) passed from person to person
at the table at Christmas dinner,
pictures what three people?*

> Jesus, Mary, Joseph.

In Sweden, what is a TOMTE*?*

> A gift-giving gnome.

What are PRESEBRAS *in Mexico?*

> Replicas of the manger scene at the nativity.

In France, what two days are the traditional gift-giving days?

> New Years Day, and December 6 (Saint Nicholas Day).

In 1997, what country was officially allowed to celebrate Christmas for the first time in 28 years?

> Cuba. Castro allowed it in honor of the first visit of Pope John Paul II.

In Spain, what do children leave in their shoes on Twelfth Night, and what do they expect in return?

On January 5, or Noche de Reys (Night of Kings), children leave barley in their shoes, to "feed" the camels of the three wise men on their way to visit the baby Jesus. When the kids awake in the morning, the barley has been "magically" replaced by candy and gifts.

What Norwegian holiday custom came from the Norse tradition of HWEOL, meaning wheel?

The Yule log. The Norse believed the sun was a wheel of fire, and lighting the Yule log celebrated the return of the sun at winter solstice. Like many other pre-Christian customs, it eventually became part of the Christmas celebration.

On Epiphany night in what European country does a benevolent old woman named "Befana" bring presents and fill stockings?

> Italy. She rides a broom and gives coal to the children who have been bad.

DER WEIHNACHTSMANN brings presents on December 6 in what country?

> "Christmas man" comes on this day in Germany; December 6 is St. Nicholas day, which is a traditional gift-giving day in many countries in Europe.

PERE NÖEL makes children happy by bringing gifts on Christmas Eve in this country.

> France. His partner, LE PERE FOUETTARD, or "Father Spanker" metes out punishment for those children who've been bad.

What is traditionally served in many Italian homes on Christmas Eve: pheasant, fish, or pork?

> Fish. Many Italian families (mostly in the south of Italy) serve seven types of fish on Christmas Eve, although the number can vary according to the custom of the region. The tradition of eating many types of fish most likely started with the Catholic Church's dietary restriction of forbidding meat to be eaten on Christmas Eve.

What word meaning "first call" is the main Christmas meal in France?

> REVEILLON. It is eaten after midnight mass on
> Christmas Eve, and features many courses.

According to the Finns, where does Santa Claus live?

> Lapland, near the Arctic Circle.

Bad children in the Czech Republic receive what from Saint Nicholas?

> Sticks.

What is the Belgian Christmas sweet bread called COUGNOU shaped like?

> The baby Jesus

Match the holiday salutation with the correct country of origin:

1) GOD JUL!
2) FROEHLICHE WEIHNACHTEN!
3) FELIZ NAVIDAD!
4) BUONE NATALE!
5) JOYEUX NOEL!
6) SROZHDESTOOM KRISTOVYM!
7) Merry Christmas!

a) Ukraine
b) United States
c) Mexico
d) France
e) Sweden
f) Italy
g) Germany

1 – e; 2– g.; 3–c; 4– f; 5– d; 6– a; 7– b.

What are the KALLIKANTZERI, who are believed to appear in Greece during the twelve days of Christmas?

Goblins. According to legend, these beings create mischief during the holidays, including climbing down the chimneys and souring milk.

*Santa Claus has many names. Can you
match the name for Santa with the
country?*

1) *JULTOMTEN*   a) *China*
2) *NISSE*   b) *England*
3) *JULERISSE*   c) *Sweden*
4) *DUN CHE LAO REN*   d) *Norway*
5) *SANTA KUROSU OJIISAN*   e) *Denmark*
6) *Father Christmas*   f) *Japan*

1 − c; 2 − e; 3 − d; 4 − a; 5 − f; 6 − b.

*How does America's Santa Claus differ
physically from England's Father
Christmas?*

Father Christmas is skinnier, according to legend.

No wonder so many Argentineans
consider this woman a saint—she
gave away 5 million toys for Christmas
in 1947.

Eva Peron.

There are believed to be thirteen of
these gift-givers in Iceland.

Santas. Thirteen, corresponding to the number to
days of Christmas, and each one has different
name. They start coming down the mountain
December 12, one by one, until the last one is
down, then it's time to celebrate Christmas. Then
they go back up the mountain, one by one, so that
by the 6th of January the Christmas season is over.

In what country is a special porridge called KUKYA eaten on Christmas Eve?

Russia. Christmas Eve dinner is meatless, but they do feast on this special porridge made of wheatberries, honey, and poppy seeds.

In Poland, when someone cries out GWIAZDKA! on Christmas Eve, what have they spotted?

GWIAZDKA, or "little star," means the first star of the night has been spotted. Poles watch the sky on Christmas Eve for this star in honor of the Star of Bethlehem.

In Spain, what do they call LA MISA DEL GALLO?

The Christmas Eve midnight mass ("the Mass of the Rooster").

In Spain, what act does the tradition HOGUERAS call for?

HOGUERAS ("bonfires"), has people jumping over fires. The practice stems from a winter solstice celebration.

What Jewish gift-giving holiday falls around the same time as Christmas?

Chanukah, or Hanukkah, which means "festival of lights." It is an eight day festival that commemorates the victory of the Maccabees and the rededication of the Jerusalem Temple, and the miracle of the oil that burned for eight days.

What African-American gift-giving holiday also is held in December?

Kwanza, (meaning first or possibly first fruit of the harvest) is celebrated from December 26 to January 1.

TASTES OF THE HOLIDAYS

Captain John Smith reported that settlers of Jamestown, Virginia consumed this rum-spiked Christmas favorite.

> *Eggnog.*

What is eggnog traditionally made from?

> *Eggs, rum, and spices.*

What exactly is "nog"?

> *Nog refers to a drink made with rum.*

Where did candy canes get their shape?

> *They were inspired by shepherd's crooks and first appeared in Europe in the 1670s. They were given to children in church to help keep them quiet.*

Made of flour and tiny candied fruit, this food seems to show up every Christmas, whether you like it or not.

Fruitcake

So, what is the deal with fruitcake anyway?

Christmas celebrations called for something sweet after the holiday meal—in the dead of winter, the only thing available was preserved fruit, so voila! fruitcake!

What nut is traditionally roasted over an open fire at Christmas time?

Chestnuts.

What are sugarplums?

> Made famous in the poem "The Night Before
> Christmas," sugarplums were originally sugar-
> coated coriander. Nowadays, they are often a
> small confection consisting of dried or candied
> fruit surrounded by icing.

What are the main ingredients in Scandinavian glogg?

> Port wine, raisins, almonds, cloves, cinnamon,
> dried fruit, dry red wine, and aquavit.

What oddly named British cabbage dish is a Boxing Day favorite?

> Bubble and squeak.

Swedish Christmas gingersnap cookies are called what?

PEPPARKAKOR.

Which of the following did George and Martha Washington partake of at their Mount Vernon Christmas dinner?
a) Roast Beef
b) Mutton Chops
c) Roast Suckling Pig
d) Roast Turkey
e) Cold Boiled Beef
f) Virginia Ham

All of them.

What is the New Year's Day treat from Holland called OLLIEBOLLEN?

A golden raisin fritter.

What is the main ingredient in the English holiday drink called "Lambs Wool"?

       Apples.

What task are Germany women performing with their WEIHNACHTS GEBACK?

       Christmas baking.

SPECULAAS, PEPERNOLEN, and TAI TAI are just a few of the cookies given to good children at Christmastime in what country?

       Holland.

According to English custom, in what direction should Christmas pudding be stirred?

> *Clockwise, for good luck.*

What is the honey cake popular during the holidays in the Ukraine called?

> *MEDIVNYK.*

What country does the cake-like dessert of JULEKAGE come from?

> *Denmark.*

How are Germany's Christmas *SPRINGERLE* cookies made?

> Dough is pressed into wooden molds that have
> different images imprinted on them. Angels,
> animals, and fruits are very popular.

Are there any plums in plum pudding?

> No. This English holiday dessert dating back to
> the middle ages contains suet, flour, sugar, raisins,
> nuts, and spices—but no plums.

What is wassail?

> It is a spiced ale or wine drunk in England at
> Christmastime. Roving bands of English people
> began strolling the streets with their wassail bowls,
> caroling, and offering the hot drink to neighbors.
> This practice became known as wassailing.

Currently, what is the most popular main course for Christmas dinner in America?

> Turkey.

What about in Great Britain during Victorian times?

> Roast Goose.

And in Whoville?

> Roast Beast. *(According to Dr. Seuss's* HOW THE GRINCH STOLE CHRISTMAS*)*

The French dessert BUCHE DE NOEL looks like an edible what?

> Log.

What Christmas delight originally contained ox-tongue?

Mince pie. 300 years ago, this English dish contained ox-tongue, chicken, eggs, sugar, raisins, and spices in a tart. Eventually the meat was excluded, and just the sweet ingredients make up the pie today. The mince refers to the minced or finely chopped meat that was traditionally included in the pie.

How was pumpkin pie originally made?

A pumpkin was hollowed out, the seeds removed, and then the pulp was stuffed back into the pumpkin, along with honey and spices, and then was baked in hot ashes.

Germans probably object to getting what fruit-filled bread as much as Americans dislike getting the ubiquitous fruitcake?

STOLLEN.

What are BUNUELOS?

> Thin round holiday pastries served in Latin
> American countries.

How do you make cranberry sauce?

> Bring fresh cranberries, sugar, and spices to a boil
> and cook for 20 minutes. Others prefer the
> traditional American route of opening a can and
> slicing up the gelled variety.

What sweet Christmas treat comes from a twisted rhizome root?

> Gingerbread. For centuries, this treat had been
> baked in Europe—sometimes as a flat cookie,
> other times as a soft cake, but almost always it was
> cut into shapes. It was bakers in Germany that
> began to use gingerbread to make LEBKUCHEEUSEL
> ("houses to nibble at").

What do you do to cider to make it "mulled"?

Steep the cider with such spices as cloves and cinnamon, and rum.

CHRISTMAS AT THE MOVIES

What was the name of the angel who showed Jimmy Stewart how rich he actually was in IT'S A WONDERFUL LIFE (1946)?

> Clarence Oddbody, played by Henry Travers. He was an angel second class (or AS2).

Who directed IT'S A WONDERFUL LIFE?

> Frank Capra.

What Sesame Street characters got their names from two minor characters in IT'S A WONDERFUL LIFE?

> Bert and Ernie. In the Capra classic, Bert was a policeman, and Ernie was a taxi driver.

What was the amount of the misplaced money that drove George to attempt suicide in IT'S A WONDERFUL LIFE?

   $8,000.

Who plays George's wife in IT'S A WONDERFUL LIFE?

   Donna Reed plays Mary.

In IT'S A WONDERFUL LIFE, what is the name of the bartender at Martini's, the bar where George tries to drown his troubles?

   Nick.

What comedy team starred in the
1934 holiday classic BABES IN TOYLAND?

>   Laurel and Hardy. The film was based on Victor
>   Herbert's operetta.

What is the video version of the movie
BABES IN TOYLAND called?

>   MARCH OF THE WOODEN SOLDIERS.

Who are Stan and Ollie trying to save
from the clutches of the evil Barnaby
in the 1934 movie BABES IN TOYLAND?

>   Little Bo Peep.

In the 1961 version of BABES IN
TOYLAND, what future Frankie Avalon
co-star played Mary Contrary?

>   Annette Funicello.

In the 1988 movie I'LL BE HOME FOR CHRISTMAS, what does Jonathan Taylor Thomas's father promise him as a Christmas gift?

A 1957 Porsche.

What Christmas gift does Melanie give Ashley when he is home on furlough in GONE WITH THE WIND?

A hand-made tunic.

The 1945 movie THE BELLS OF ST. MARY'S starred Bing Crosby, playing opposite this CASABLANCA beauty.

Ingrid Bergman, as Sister Benedict.

Which composer wrote the score to the Bing Crosby 1954 holiday movie WHITE CHRISTMAS?

> Irving Berlin.

Who played the two male leads, Phil and Bob, in WHITE CHRISTMAS?

> Danny Kaye and Bing Crosby.

Who played the two female leads, Betty and Judy, in WHITE CHRISTMAS?

> Rosemary Clooney and Vera-Ellen.

What holiday movie featured the song "White Christmas" for the first time?

> HOLIDAY INN (1942).

Who competed for Marjorie Reynolds' affections in HOLIDAY INN (1942)?

Fred Astaire and Bing Crosby.

In the 1940 movie BEYOND TOMORROW, on what special night do the two young lovers, James and Jean, meet?

Christmas Eve.

In the 1947 movie THE BISHOP'S WIFE, who plays the angel who helps the Bishop (played by David Niven) recapture the spirit of Christmas?

Cary Grant.

What is the angel's name in THE BISHOP'S WIFE?

Dudley.

*The 1947 movie BUSH CHRISTMAS, is set
in what "down under" country?*

> *Australia.*

*What famous silent movie director
directed the 1908 short THE CHRISTMAS
BURGLARS?*

> *D.W. Griffith.*

*1945's CHRISTMAS IN CONNECTICUT stars
what actress playing a food columnist
that can't cook?*

> *Barbara Stanwyck.*

What legal problem is Santa Claus facing in The Christmas That Almost Wasn't ?

> Santa was threatened with eviction in this 1965 film.

In the 1984 thriller, Don't Open Till Christmas, what kind of people is a serial killer stalking?

> Anyone in a Santa suit.

Carol for Another Christmas, the 1964 "United Nations Special" was this All About Eve director's first work for television.

> Joseph Mankiewicz.

In ERNEST SAVES CHRISTMAS, what problem is Ernest trying to help Santa Claus solve?

Picking a successor.

What character has been played by Shirley Temple, Elsbeth Sigmund, Jennifer Edwards and Noely Thornton?

Heidi. 1937, 1952, 1968 (TV), 1993 (TV).

What 1949 movie starring Robert Mitchum and Janet Leigh wooed movie-goers with ads that stated "Baby, you're just what I want for Christmas"?

HOLIDAY AFFAIR.

What face slapping young whipper-snapper was left HOME ALONE for the holidays in 1990?

> *Macaulay Culkin as Kevin McCallister.*

In HOME ALONE, what country was Kevin's family flying to when they realized they had left a member of the family back home?

> *France.*

In the 1972 thriller HOME FOR THE HOLIDAYS starring Sally Field, why does the patriarch of the family call his three daughters home for Christmas?

> *He wants them to kill his new wife, who he suspects is trying to poison him.*

What star, usually known for her dancing, played a convict on leave for Christmas in the 1944 movie I'LL BE SEEING YOU?

Ginger Rogers.

Fred Astaire plays eight different characters, including Santa Claus, in what 1978 made for TV movie?

THE MAN IN THE SANTA CLAUS SUIT.

The 1991 movie MIDNIGHT CLEAR had soldiers from two opposing sides come together at Christmas during what war?

American and German soldiers tried to put aside their differences during this World War II movie.

1994's MIXED NUTS stars Steve Martin trying to get through a very hot Christmas in what state?

> California.

What family returned to the big screen in the National Lampoon sequel CHRISTMAS VACATION in 1989?

> The Griswolds. This sequel had Chevy Chase returning as the head of the hapless Griswold family.

Who plays Cousin Eddie in CHRISTMAS VACATION?

> Randy Quaid.

What toy delivers the star to the top of the tree in the 1933 film THE NIGHT BEFORE CHRISTMAS?

A toy blimp.

What animated cat and mouse team starred in the 1941 short THE NIGHT BEFORE CHRISTMAS?

Tom and Jerry.

Which of Santa's reindeer lends its name to the 1989 movie about a young girl who helps an injured reindeer?

Prancer.

The 1916 silent movie THE RIGHT TO BE HAPPY is based on what Dickens classic?

A Christmas Carol.

What horror movie centered around Christmastime has sparked five sequels?

> *SILENT NIGHT, DEADLY NIGHT (1984).*

What Christmas song starts off the action movie LETHAL WEAPON?

> *"Jingle Bell Rock."*

What do Albert Finney, Patrick Stewart, George C. Scott, Bill Murray, Jack Palance, Fred Flinstone, Beavis, and Mr. Magoo have in common?

> *They all have played characters in the movies and on TV based on Dickens's famous sour-puss Ebenezer Scrooge.*

What was the first full-length film adaptation of A CHRISTMAS CAROL?

The 1935 English movie starring Seymor Hicks, called Scrooge.

What was different about the 1970 movie Scrooge from all the previous movie version of A CHRISTMAS CAROL?

It was a musical. It starred Albert Finney as the title character, and earned four Oscar nominations.

What 1983 Christmas movie, narrated by Peter Billingsley, was based on a short story by Jean Shepherd?

A CHRISTMAS STORY. The story appeared in Jean Shepherd's collection IN GOD WE TRUST, ALL OTHERS PAY CASH.

What did Ralphie, the main character in A CHRISTMAS STORY, want more than anything for Christmas?

> *A Red Ryder BB gun.*

What did all the adults in Ralpie's life insist would happen if he received this much coveted present?

> *"You'll shoot your eye out!"*

What department store did Santa work for in the 1947 movie MIRACLE ON 34TH STREET?

> *Macy's.*

Who played the little girl who didn't believe in Santa in this movie?

> *Natalie Wood.*

What knighted actor played Kris Kringle in the 1994 version of MIRACLE ON 34TH STREET?

Sir Richard Attenborough.

What star of the Naked Gun series plays Santa in the 1991 movie ALL I WANT FOR CHRISTMAS?

Leslie Neilson.

Tim Burton's Jack Skellinton longed to leave Halloween Town for the pleasures of Christmas in what 1993 animated film?

THE NIGHTMARE BEFORE CHRISTMAS. (Burton used stop-motion animation techniques similar to the beloved TV holiday favorite RUDOLPH THE RED-NOSED REINDEER.)

In his first big screen leading role, Tim Allen accidentally kills Santa Claus in what 1994 movie?

> THE SANTA CLAUSE. *Tim's character puts on the deceased Santa's suit, and begins turning into the jolly old man, both physically and emotionally.*

Bruce Willis finds himself taking on greedy terrorists on Christmas Eve in what 1988 action movie?

> DIE HARD.

What Preston Sturges 1940 film has "Christmas" placed in the wrong month?

> CHRISTMAS IN JULY. *Starring Dick Powell, it is a comedy about a man who goes on a shopping spree after being fooled into thinking he has won a large amount of money.*

What action hero takes on some heavy-duty holiday shopping to find his son a Turbo Man action figure in the 1996 film JINGLE ALL THE WAY?

Arnold Schwarzenegger.

What is Arnold Schwarzenegger's occupation in JINGLE ALL THE WAY?

Mattress salesman.

Santa takes on some pesky aliens in what absurd 1964 "B" movie?

SANTA CLAUS CONQUERS THE MARTIANS.

What movie featured Judy Garland warbling "Have Yourself a Merry Little Christmas"?

MEET ME IN ST. LOUIS (1944).

Yellow contacts and a lot of green fur transformed what funny man into the title character of the 2000 movie HOW THE GRINCH STOLE CHRISTMAS?

Jim Carrey. The rubber-faced actor spent five hours a day in the makeup chair to get into character for this holiday movie.

Who directed this 2000 movie adaptation of Dr. Suess' beloved holiday tale?

Ron Howard.

**The creators of South Park featured
what two people fighting in their
internet-only animated short THE
SPIRIT OF CHRISTMAS?**

> Santa and Jesus. It's ice-skater Brian Boytano that
> eventually settles the dispute in a peaceful
> manner.

**What popular Christmas song was
introduced in the 1951 movie THE
LEMON DROP KID starring Bob Hope?**

> "Silver Bells," written by the team of Jay Livingston
> and Ray Evans.

**Dennis Leary holds an annoying
family hostage on Christmas Eve in
what 1994 comedy?**

> THE REF.

What festive name does Jim Carrey's character sport in the 1994 film DUMB AND DUMBER?

Lloyd Christmas.

What villain in the 1992 sequel BATMAN RETURNS *planned to ruin Gotham City's grand Christmas celebration?*

The Penguin, played by a flipper-fingered Danny DeVito.

In the 1988 movie SCROOGED, *what is the Ebenezer-like character Frank Cross's job?*

He is a TV network executive, played by Bill Murray.

What ill-spirited holiday order does the Sheriff of Nottingham bark out in the 1991 movie ROBIN HOOD: PRINCE OF THIEVES?

> *"Cancel Christmas!" Alan Rickman's over-the-top portrayal of the villainous Sheriff is reason enough to catch this movie.*

What 1968 film starring Peter O'Toole and Katharine Hepburn takes place during Christmas in the year 1183 at the Castle of Chinon?

> *THE LION IN WINTER. The film focuses on the love/hate relationship between King Henry II and his Queen, Eleanor of Aquitaine. For her portrayal as Eleanor Katharine Hepburn shared the Best Actress Academy Award with Barbara Streisand that year.*

What 1974 movie musical featured the song "We Need a Little Christmas," and was Lucille Ball's last film appearance?

> MAME.

What actress received the news that she had won the role of a lifetime on Christmas Day, 1938?

> Vivien Leigh was told that she had beaten out the likes of Lana Turner, Bette Davis, and Joan Crawford for the role of Scarlett O'Hara in GONE WITH THE WIND.

CHRISTMAS ON THE
SMALL SCREEN

What Peanuts Christmas favorite first aired on CBS in 1965?

> A CHARLIE BROWN CHRISTMAS. This much-loved cartoon illustrates perfectly the true meaning of Christmas, and has aired yearly ever since.

Who picks out the sparse-looking Christmas tree instead of the requested shiny aluminum one in A CHARLIE BROWN CHRISTMAS?

> Charlie Brown.

Who is the director of the play in A CHARLIE BROWN CHRISTMAS?

> Charlie Brown.

Which character delivers the moving speech at the end of *A Charlie Brown Christmas* that explains the true meaning of Christmas?

> *Linus.*

What Brady kid did not return for the Christmas reunion special *A Very Brady Christmas*?

> *Cindy, originally played by Susan Olsen, was played by Jennifer Runyon for the 1988 TV special.*

What profession was Bobby trying to hide from his parents in *A Very Brady Christmas*?

> *Racecar driver.*

Which Brady had become a doctor?

> Greg.

**Who was the deep-voiced narrator of
the classic 1966 television cartoon
HOW THE GRINCH STOLE CHRISTMAS?**

> The famous horror movie actor Boris Karloff, best
> known for Frankenstein.

**Who narrated the made for TV special
RUDOLPH THE RED-NOSED REINDEER
(1964)?**

> Burl Ives, in the character of "Sam the Snowman."

Although he didn't get to sing "Inka Dinka Do," this actor did get to narrate the cartoon FROSTY THE SNOWMAN *in 1969.*

Jimmy Durante.

Although he may be best known as Opie's dad, this actor was the narrator of the cartoon sequel FROSTY'S WINTER WONDERLAND *(1976).*

Andy Griffith.

Who narrated the 1970 cartoon SANTA CLAUS IS COMING TO TOWN, *a man known more for his dance moves than his voice?*

Fred Astaire.

**In the 1964 TV classic RUDOLPH THE
RED-NOSED REINDEER, what career
does Rudolph's elf-friend Herbie want
to give up Santa's workshop for?**

> Dentistry. According to the other elves, Herbie
> "doesn't like to make toys."

**What land do Rudolph and Herbie
visit after they run away from the
North Pole?**

> The Land of Misfit Toys. These slightly askew toys
> just want children to play with them. Luckily for
> them, Rudolph doesn't forget them on Christmas
> Eve.

**Who is Rudolph's father according to
1964's RUDOLPH THE RED-NOSED
REINDEER?**

> Donner.

Who was the traveling prospector Rudolph and Herbie meet in their travels?

> *Yukon Cornelius.*

What sequel to RUDOLPH THE RED-NOSED REINDEER *has Rudolph searching for the missing Baby New Year?*

> *RUDOLPH'S SHINY NEW YEAR (1975). Rudolph and friends must save the Baby New Year from an evil buzzard named Aeon.*

How did Thurl Ravenscroft contribute to the TV cartoon HOW THE GRINCH STOLE CHRISTMAS?

> He lent his deep voice to the song "You're a Mean One, Mr. Grinch." Thurl is also known for his work as Tony the Tiger® in cereal commercials ("They're Grrrrrrrreat!")

What does the Grinch use to pull his sleigh?

> His dog, Max.

Mary Kate and Ashley Olsen starred in this 1992 Christmas special when they were only six years old.

> TO GRANDMOTHER'S HOUSE WE GO.

What buxom county singer starred in
A SMOKEY MOUNTAIN CHRISTMAS in 1986?

Dolly Parton starred in this made for TV movie.

What former Charlie's Angel helps
save Santa's North Pole Village in THE
NIGHT THEY SAVED CHRISTMAS?

Jaclyn Smith starred in this 1984 TV movie.

In the 1990 TV movie A MOM FOR
CHRISTMAS, what comes to life after the
wish of a little girl?

A mannequin, played by Olivia Newton-John.

The 1977 TV movie IT HAPPENED ONE
CHRISTMAS is a remake of what
favorite Frank Capra holiday movie?

> *IT'S A WONDERFUL LIFE.*

Who plays the Jimmy Stewart role in
this remake?

> *Marlo Thomas plays Mary Bailey Hatch.*

What CITIZEN KANE star plays the evil
Mr. Potter in this remake?

> *Orson Wells.*

What city does Mickey Rooney want to
show his grandson at Christmastime
in IT CAME UPON THE MIDNIGHT CLEAR?

> *New York City, in this 1984 TV movie.*

Who plays the crotchety father who refuses to get into the Christmas spirit in THE HOUSE WITHOUT A CHRISTMAS TREE?

> Jason Robards starred in this 1972 TV movie.

In the 1980 TV movie GUESS WHO'S COMING FOR CHRISTMAS, where does the strange visitor played by Beau Bridges claim he is from?

> Outer space.

What twist does the 1995 TV movie Ebbie put on the retelling of Dickens's A CHRISTMAS CAROL?

> The Ebenezer Scrooge character is a woman, Elizabeth "Ebbie" Scrooge, played by Susan Lucci.

The 1992 made for TV remake of
CHRISTMAS IN CONNECTICUT was
directed by what TERMINATOR star?

Arnold Schwarzenegger.

What actress plays the lead role in
the 1992 made for TV remake of
CHRISTMAS IN CONNECTICUT?

Dyan Cannon.

**What *LITTLE HOUSE ON THE PRAIRIE*
child star plays Kelly Sullivan in
*CHRISTMAS MIRACLE IN CAUFIELD,
U.S.A.*, the 1977 made for TV movie?**

> *Melissa Gilbert.*

**CHRISTMAS ON DIVISION STREET *teaches
what *WONDER YEARS* actor an
important lesson about caring for
the homeless?**

> *Fred Savage starred in this 1991 made for
> TV movie.*

**What former *DUKES OF HAZZARD* stars
play brothers in the 1987 TV movie
CHRISTMAS COMES TO WILLOW CREEK?**

> *John Schneider and Tom Wopat.*

*What "Rocky Mountain High" singer
starred in the 1986 TV movie THE
CHRISTMAS GIFT?*

John Denver.

*In the 1986 TV version of BABES IN
TOYLAND, what future star of the
Matrix played Jack-be-Nimble?*

Keanu Reeves.

*What English actor reprised his
Blackadder role in the 1988 TV movie
BLACKADDER'S CHRISTMAS CAROL?*

Rowan Atkinson, playing Ebenezer Blackadder, a
kind, gentle man who is turned miserly after
seeing visions of his ancestors and descendants and
deciding "Bad guys have all the fun."

What actor, best known as The Fonz, starred in the 1979 TV movie AN AMERICAN CHRISTMAS CAROL?

Henry Winkler played Benedict Slade.

Who was his miserly character based on?

Ebenezer Scrooge.

Where was the first televised midnight Christmas mass held?

> Saint Patrick's Cathedral in New York City in 1948.

What is the name of the Simpson family dog?

> Santa's Little Helper.

Berkeley Breathed brought his BLOOM COUNTY comic strip characters Opus and Bill to life in a 1991 animated Christmas special. What Christmas miracle did Opus wish for?

> Wings that work. Opus is a penguin fighting his evolutionary flightlessness.

What twist on IT'S A WONDERFUL LIFE did the television show MARRIED WITH CHILDREN come up with in their 1992 Christmas episode?

> *An angel shows Al what life would have been like if he had never been born. Instead of the awful visions Jimmy Stewart was shown, Al's family and friends would be much happier without him. And that alone convinces him to return and make their lives miserable.*

In the 1974 animated TV special THE YEAR WITHOUT A SANTA CLAUS, what kind of Christmas does the Heat Miser want?

> *A green one. The Snow Miser wanted a white Christmas, of course.*

What Jim Henson Christmas special involved a talent competition in Frog Town Hollow?

EMMET OTTER'S JUG-BAND CHRISTMAS (1977).

On SEINFELD, what does George's dad prefer to celebrate instead of Christmas?

Festivus, a holiday Mr. Costanza invented himself.

What does Ralph Kramden hock in order to get Alice a better present on THE HONEYMOONERS episode "'Twas the Night Before Christmas"?

His beloved bowling ball. But he does manage to learn a lesson about the true meaning of Christmas.

What year did Bing Crosby begin his annual Christmas TV specials?

1961. Bing had done radio specials since 1936, and appeared with Frank Sinatra in a TV Christmas special in 1957, but his annual show didn't begin until 1961. The specials lasted until his death in 1977.

HOLIDAY MUSIC

What follows the line "God rest ye merry gentleman" in the carol of the same name?

> "Let nothing ye dismay."

In the carol "God Rest Ye Merry Gentlemen," why are the gentlemen so tired?

> Actually, they aren't. In this song, the word "rest" means "keep."

What kind of tidings are offered in "God Rest Ye Merry Gentlemen"?

> Comfort and joy.

Where are the "hopes and fears of all the years" met?

> Bethlehem, according to the song "Oh Little Town of Bethlehem."

Finish the next line from "O Little Town of Bethlehem": "Above thy deep and dreamless sleep..."

> "The silent stars go by."

What George Frederick Handel hymn involves shepherds doing their jobs?

> "While Shepherds Watched Their Flocks."

In the song "Oh Come All Ye Faithful,"
where exactly should the faithful come?

> Bethlehem.

Sing the chorus of "O Come All Ye
Faithful."

> "O come let us adore Him,
> O come let us adore Him,
> O come let us adore Him,
> Christ the Lord."

The writer of "Hark! The Herald
Angles Sing" is often considered the
"greatest hymn writer of all ages."
Name him.

> Charles Wesley (1707–1788). He wrote over
> 6,500 hymns.

Who are reconciled in "Hark! The Herald Angels Sing"?

God and sinners.

What should "ev'ry heart" do in the carol "Joy to the World"?

"Prepare Him room."

What do heaven and nature do according to the song "Joy to the World"?

Sing.

"The cattle are lowing
The poor baby wakes
But little Lord Jesus
No crying he makes."
Name the title of this hymn.

"Away in the Manger."

In the hymn *"Away in the Manger,"*
where is the little Lord Jesus sleeping?

In the hay.

In the hymn *"What Child is This,"*
where is the Christ child sleeping?

On Mary's lap.

William Dix set his hymn "What Child is This" to what song from the 1500s?

> "Greensleeves."

What quiet carol did Joseph Mohr write and perform for the first time at a Midnight Mass in 1818?

> "Stille Nacht! Heilige Nacht!," known in English as "Silent Night."

What instrument was "Silent Night" originally written for?

> The guitar.

What two lines follow "Silent Night,
holy night; all is calm, all is bright"
from "Silent Night"?

> *"'Round yon Virgin mother and child*
> *Holy infant so tender and mild."*

What do the "Heav'nly hosts" sing in
"Silent Night"?

> *"Hallelujah."*

How many times is the word "noel"
repeated in "The First Noel"?

> *21 times. Four times at the end of each of the five*
> *stanzas, plus once in the first line of the first*
> *stanza.*

What is the last line of "The First Noel"?

> *"Born is the King of Israel."*

Name the carol that contains the following chorus:
"O, Star of wonder star of night,
Star with royal beauty bright,
Westward leading, still proceeding,
Guide us to thy perfect light."

> *"We Three Kings."*

What period of time does the song "The Twelve Days of Christmas" cover?

> *Christmas Day (December 25th) to January 5th.*
> *January 6th is the start of Epiphany.*

*Match the gift from "my true love" for
the day of Christmas from the song
"The Twelve Days of Christmas"*

1) 1st day of Christmas   a) French hens
2) 2nd day of Christmas   b) geese a laying
3) 3rd day of Christmas   c) drummers drumming
4) 4th day of Christmas   d) pipers piping
5) 5th day of Christmas   e) partridge in a pear tree
6) 6th day of Christmas   f) maids a milking
7) 7th day of Christmas   g) golden rings
8) 8th day of Christmas   h) calling birds
9) 9th day of Christmas   I) lords a leaping
10) 10th day of Christmas j) swans a swimming
11) 11th day of Christmas k) ladies dancing
12) 12th day of Christmas m) turtle doves

1 – e; 2 – m; 3 – a; 4 – h; 5 – g; 6 – b; 7 – j;
8 – f; 9 – k; 10 – I; 11 – d; 12 – c

What Christmas carol begins with the lines "Hark how the bells, sweet silver bells, all seem to say, throw cares away"?

> *"Carol of the Bells."*

What southern rock group sang the song "Christmas in Dixie"?

> *Alabama.*

What line comes after "Our cheeks are nice and rosy and comfy cozy are we" in the carol "Sleigh Ride"?

> *"We're snuggled up together like two birds of a feather would be."*

In the song "Sleigh Ride," what two
famous printmakers does the song
invoke?

> Currier and Ives.

What question is asked in the first
lines of "Auld Lang Syne"?

> "Should auld acquaintance be forgot and never
> brought to mind?"

What Scottish poet wrote the words to
"Auld Lang Syne"?

> Robert Burns.

What carol's refrain is "Gloria in
Excelsis Deo"?

> "Angels We Have Heard on High."

What "Man in Black" had a 1980 Christmas album called CLASSIC CHRISTMAS?

Johnny Cash.

What song was Bing Crosby talking about when he said "it inspires a happy sadness in the heart"?

"White Christmas."

What line follows "May your days be merry and bright" in the song "White Christmas"?

"And may all your Christmases be white."

When does the carol "Good King Wenceslas" take place?

> On the Feast of Stephen (St. Stephen's day, December 26).

How is the frost described in the song "Good King Wenceslas"?

> Cruel.

Where was the real "Good King Wenceslas" king?

> Bohemia. He became a Christian martyr when he was killed by his younger brother for the throne.

The last two lines of "Good King Wenceslas" present a good holiday lesson. What are they?

> *"Ye who now will bless the poor, Shall yourselves find blessing."*

What is it recommended that you deck the halls with?

> *Boughs of holly. ("Deck the Halls.")*

How many times is "la" sung in one line of "Deck the Halls"?

> *Eight.*

"Deck the Halls" originated in what country?

> *Wales.*

James Pierpont wrote what favorite Christmas carol in 1850?

> *"Jingle Bells." Pierpont was the uncle of J. P. Morgan.*

What was the original title of "Jingle Bells"?

> *"One Horse Open Sleigh"*

What is the name of the horse that pulls the sleigh in "Jingle Bells"?

> *Bobtail.*

In what country did the carol "O Christmas Tree" originate?

> *Germany.*

What line follows "Fall on you knees" from the hymn "O Holy Night"?

"O hear the angel voices."

What are the names of the two children mentioned in "Up On the Housetop"?

Nell and Will.

What will Santa put in each of their stockings?

For little Nell, a dolly that laughs and cries. For Will, a hammer and plastic tacks, as well as a ball and a game of jacks.

What kind of harps do the angels have in "It Came Upon a Midnight Clear"?

> Gold.

What Christmas song ends with the lines "Santy Claus, Santy Claus, just listen to my plea, I don't want nothing for Christmas but my baby back to me"?

> "Santa Claus Blues," recorded by the Red Onion Jazz Babies in 1924, written by Charley Straight and Gus Kahn.

What crooner had a hit in 1958 with "Winter Wonderland"?

> Johnny Mathis.

In "Winter Wonderland" what two things will we pretend Mr. Snowman is?

Parson Brown, and a circus clown.

What British monarch began the tradition of standing during the "Hallelujah Chorus" of Handel's Messiah?

George II. Theories abound on the reason why he stood during the chorus, ranging from the King being so moved by the piece of music that he couldn't stay seated, to having fallen asleep during the performance and jumped up because he was startled awake by the loud music.

According to "Frosty the Snowman,"
what are Frosty's eyes made of?

> Coal.

How about his nose?

> A button.

What kind of pipe does Frosty smoke?

> Corncob.

What type of hat did Frosty the
Snowman sport?

> Aside being magical (for it did bring him to life)
> it was a silk hat.

When does most of the action in the opera LA BOHEME take place?

> Christmas Eve.

What musical Christmas practice did Oliver Cromwell put a stop to in England in the 1640s?

> Singing carols. Apparently Cromwell decided that the singing sounded too much like people having fun.

What tradition did the Greek dance called a CHORAULEIN eventually become?

> Caroling. The dancer was originaly accompanied by a flute. The French modified the tradition, and replaced the flute with singing. By the 1600's it was only singing, and usually at Christmas.

*How many ships came "sailing in" on
Christmas Day in the morning?*

> Three. ("I Saw Three Ships")

*What Christmas tune do those
annoying barking dogs belt out?*

> "Jingle Bells."

*The Kinks beseeched what man to
"give us some money" in 1977?*

> "Father Christmas."

*The odd paring of Bing Crosby
and David Bowie created what
unforgettable Christmas song remake?*

> *"The Little Drummer Boy." The duet was performed
> on Crosby's annual Christmas TV special in 1977.
> It is also played on MTV each holiday season.*

*What kind of Christmas did Elvis plan
to have, without you?*

> *Blue. ("Blue Christmas.")*

*Bob Geldof and a bevy of music
celebs asked what musical question
for African famine relief?*

> *"Do They Know It's Christmas?" The 1984 Band
> Aid song featured the voices of George Michael,
> Phil Collins, and Bono, among others.*

What song wishes you a Merry Christmas in Spanish?

> *"Feliz Navidad."*

Who got run over by a reindeer?

> *Grandma, according to that holiday classic "Grandma Got Run Over By a Reindeer."*

In what Christmas song did Don Henley claim to "have no friends to wish me greetings, once again"?

> *"Bells Will Be Ringing."*

What should you go tell on the mountain?

> *"Jesus Christ is born." You should also tell it over the hills, and everywhere as well.*

In the song "Have Yourself a Merry Little Christmas," what should you hang upon the highest bough?

A shining star.

What is the "prettiest sight to see" according to the song "It's Beginning to Look a Lot Like Christmas"?

"The holly that will be on your own front door."

Who was seen kissing Santa Claus under the mistletoe?

Mommy. ("I Saw Mommy Kissing Santa Claus.")

According to "Jingle Bell Rock," jingle bell time is a swell time to do what?

"Go gliding in a one horse sleigh."

Finish the next two lines:
"Oh the weather outside is frightful
But the fire is so delightful…"

> *"And since we've no place to go, let it snow! Let it snow! Let it snow!"*

How is everyone dancing in the song
"Rockin' Around the Christmas Tree"?

> *"Merrily," and in "the new old-fashioned way."*

What is on the B side of Bruce
Springsteen's 1986 single "War"?

> *"Merry Christmas Baby." The year before, Bruce released the single "My Hometown" with "Santa Claus is Comin' to Town" on the B side.*

What Tchaikovsky ballet, always a
Christmas favorite, features a Sugar
Plum Fairy and a Rat King?

THE NUTCRACKER.

What Christmas extravaganza, held
every year in New York City, stars the
leggy Rockettes?

The Radio City Christmas Spectacular.

What was Brenda Lee rockin' around?

The Christmas tree. ("Rockin' Around the
Christmas Tree.")

What did Chuck Berry urge one of
Santa's reindeer to do?

"Run, Run Rudolph."

Whose 1988 Christmas album collection released on Rhino records was entitled SANTA'S GOT A BRAND NEW BAG?

> James Brown.

What was Rudolph banned from playing?

> Reindeer games, according to "Rudolph the Red Nosed Reindeer."

In "Santa Baby" Eartha Kitt asked Santa to bring her one of these, in light blue.

> A '54 convertible.

What does the all-seeing Santa not want you to do in "Santa Claus is Coming to Town"?

> *Cry, pout.*

In the Jackson 5's rendition of "Up on the Housetop," what does Tito want Santa to bring him?

> *A new guitar. He also wants a guarantee that it will play in tune.*

In a tune Bing Crosby made popular, what will you hear on "every street corner" during Christmas?

> *"Silver Bells."*

What is the name of the song that begins "Chestnuts roasting on an open fire"?

"The Christmas Song," written by Mel Torme.

The carolers in "We Wish You a Merry Christmas" won't go until they get what?

Figgy pudding.

How is the star's tail described in "Do You Hear What I Hear"?

It is as big as a kite.

What is the subtitle to the John Lennon's song "Happy Christmas"?

> War is Over.

What is "everyone telling you" in the song "The Most Wonderful Time of the Year"?

> "Be of good cheer."

What Latin heartthrob did Rosie O'Donnell recruit to sing "Ay, Ay, Ay It's Christmas" on her album ANOTHER ROSIE CHRISTMAS?

> Ricky Martin. This was the second Christmas album that Rosie put out—all of the proceeds from her albums are donated to the For All Kids Foundation.

What high-voiced rodents actually topped the pop charts with their rendition of "Christmas Don't Be Late"?

> Alvin and the Chipmunks. (Alvin, Simon and Theodore, who sang along with Dave Seville.)

What four young amphibians wished us a "Turtle Christmas" in the mid-1990s?

> Leonardo, Raphael, Michaelangelo, and Donatello, otherwise known as the Teenage Mutant Ninja Turtles.

Match the artist with their Christmas album:

1) *Mannheim Steamroller*
2) *Enya*
3) **Nsync*
4) *Kenny G*
5) *Toni Braxton*
6) *Garth Brooks*
7) *Jim Brickman*
8) *Vince Guaraldi Trio*

a) CHARLIE BROWN
   CHRISTMAS
b) THE CHRISTMAS ED
c) THE GIFT
d) HOME FOR CHRISTMAS
e) RENAISSANCE HOLIDAY
f) SNOWFLAKES
g) FAITH
h) THE MAGIC OF
   CHRISTMAS

1 – e; 2 – b; 3 – d; 4 – g; 5 – f;
6 – h; 7 – c; 8 – a,

In "Here Comes Santa Claus" what street is Santa coming down?

    Santa Claus Lane.

Name the three tenors featured on the album THREE TENORS CHRISTMAS.

    Jose Carreras, Placido Domingo, and
    Luciano Pavarotti.

What super trio released their Christmas album, 8 Days of Christmas, in 2001?

Destiny's Child. The album featured Christmas classics like "White Christmas" and "O Holy Night," along with some new songs written by the members.

CHRISTMAS POEMS,
BOOKS AND LITERATURE

What was the original title of the poem "The Night Before Christmas"?

"An Account of a Visit From Saint Nicholas."

Who wrote "The Night Before Christmas"?

Clement Clarke Moore wrote the poem for his children in 1822. Moore did not own up to writing the poem until 1837, fearing for his intellectual reputation.

In "The Night Before Christmas," what were the parents wearing on their heads?

A kerchief and a cap.

In this famous poem, what items are St. Nick's cheeks and nose compared to?

> Roses and a cherry, respectively.

What is the last line of "An Account of a Visit from St. Nicholas"?

> "Happy Christmas to all, and to all a good-night!"

Who wrote the classic story about the true nature of giving, "The Gift of the Magi."

> O. Henry.

*How much did Della have to spend on
her husband in "The Gift of the
Magi"?*

$1.87.

*What does Della sell to buy a watch
fob chain in "The Gift of the Magi"?*

Her hair.

*What does Jim sell to buy a hair comb
in "The Gift of the Magi"?*

His watch.

*In O. Henry's "The Gift of the Magi,"
how much did Della and Jim's flat cost
them?*

$8 per week, furnished.

What poet, sister of two famous pre-Raphaelite artists, wrote the poem "What Can I Give Him?"

> *"What can I give Him, poor as I am?*
> *If I were a shepherd, I would bring a lamb.*
> *If I were a Wise Man, I would do my part,*
> *Yet what can I give Him, give my heart."*
> —Christina Rossetti.

"A Christmas Dinner Won in Battle" is a short story written by what Red Badge of Courage author?

Stephen Crane.

What Wizard of Oz creator wrote the children's stories "A Kidnapped Santa Claus" and "The Story of Santa Claus"?

L. Frank Baum.

What creator of THROUGH THE LOOKING GLASS wrote the poem "Christmas Greeting From a Fairy to a Child"?

Lewis Carroll.

THE ADVENTURE OF THE BLUE CARBUNCLE featured what famous Arthur Conan Doyle detective in a story with a Christmas twist?

Sherlock Holmes.

THE ADVENTURE OF CHRISTMAS PUDDING featured what famous Agatha Christie detective?

Hercule Poirot.

What Scarlet Letter author published
THE CHRISTMAS BANQUET in 1843?

> Nathaniel Hawthorne.

What country did Rudyard Kipling
write about in his Christmas poem?

> India, in "Christmas in India."

What GUYS AND DOLLS author wrote
the short story "Dancing Dan's
Christmas"?

> Damon Runyon.

To what does the title of Shakespeare's play TWELFTH NIGHT refer?

Critics have many theories, but one of the most prevalent is that it may refer to the twelfth day of the Christmas season, marked by the Feast of Epiphany.

What poet wrote the poem "little tree," which begins with the lines: "little tree /little silent Christmas tree/ you are so little…"?

e. e. cummings.

What famous Shakespeare play does the following quote come from?

"Some say that ever 'gainst that season comes
Wherein our Saviour's birth is celebrated,
The bird of dawning singeth all night long…"
HAMLET, Act 1, Scene 1.

*Match the first line of each poem with
the title and author on the next page:*

1) *"Immensity cloistered in thy dear wom"*
2) *"Christmas Eve, and twelve of the clock"*
3) *"'Twas the night before Christmas"*
4) *"This is the Month, and this the happy morn"*
5) *"The threefold terror of love; a fallen flare"*
6) *"Look there at the star!"*
7) *"Three kings came riding from far away"*
8) *"Their time past, pulled down"*

a) "The Oxen,"
  Thomas Hardy
b) "Burning the Christmas Greens,"
  William Carlos Williams
c) "The Three Kings,"
  Henry Wadsworth Longfellow
d) "A Visit From St. Nicholas,"
  Clement Moore
e) "The Mother of God,"
  William Butler Yeats
f) "On the Morning of Christ's Nativity,"
  John Milton
g) "Nativity" and "Annunciation,"
  John Donne
h) "Shepherd's Song at Christmas,"
  Langston Hughes

  1 – g; 2 – a; 3 – d; 4 – f; 5 – e; 6 – h;
  7 – c; 8 – b.

Name the character who said "Maybe Christmas…doesn't come from a store. Maybe Christmas, perhaps, means a little bit more."

> The Grinch, after his change of heart in Dr. Seuss's HOW THE GRINCH STOLE CHRISTMAS.

What color was the Grinch?

> Green.

When was Dr. Seuss's HOW THE GRINCH STOLE CHRISTMAS first published?

> 1957. At the time, it set records for children's book sales.

What author of A CHRISTMAS CAROL
also wrote the short story "The Story
of the Goblins Who Stole a Sexton"?

> Charles Dickens, found in the collection CHRISTMAS STORIES. According to the final passage, "this story has at least one moral...and that is, that if a man turn sulky and drink by himself at Christmas time, he may make up his mind to be not a bit better for it."

What Walter de la Mare poem centers
around a romantic Christmas custom?

> "Mistletoe."

What saint's history is uncovered in
Booth Tarkington's short story
"Christmas This Year"?

> St. Nicholas.

What famous first lady wrote about her favorite memories of the holidays in "Christmas at Hyde Park"?

Eleanor Roosevelt.

Ogden Nash's poem "A Carol For Children" is based on what popular Christmas carol?

"God Rest Ye Merry Gentlemen."

How does Nash's poem begin?

"God rest you merry, Innocents,
Let nothing you dismay,
Let nothing wound an eager heart
Upon this Christmas day."

*What LITTLE WOMEN author also
penned the short story "A Christmas
Dream, and How It Came True"?*

Louisa May Alcott.

*What "Road Not Taken" poet wrote
"Christmas Trees: A Christmas
Circular Letter"?*

Robert Frost.

*Christmastime in what city does
Norman Vincent Peale write about in
"A Gift of the Heart"?*

New York City.

Around what post-holiday activity does W. H. Auden's poem "Well, So That is That" center?

> Taking down the Christmas tree.

Name the Scottish poet who wrote these lines:
"The damsel donned her kirtle shein
The hall was dressed wih holly green.
Forth to the wood did merry men go
To gather in the mistletoe."

> Sir Walter Scott,
> from "Christmas Eve in the Olden Time."

"A good conscience is a
continual Christmas."
Name the famous American to
whom this quote is attributed.

Benjamin Franklin.

Best known for her WRINKLE IN TIME
series, what author also wrote "O
Simplicitas," a poem about the Virgin
Mary?

Madeleine L'Engle.

Who wrote the children's short story,
"The Nutcracker"?

E. T. A. Hoffmann.

Who are the children in this favorite holiday story?

Fritz and Marie.

Whose short story "Christmas Song" features a character named Simple?

Langston Hughes.

What is the last name of Joe, one of the characters from Faulkner's LIGHT IN AUGUST?

Christmas.

What Dickens' novel has a chapter entitled "The Christmas Chapter"?

THE PICKWICK PAPERS.

*Best known today for the scary
"Legend of Sleepy Hollow," what
author is credited for helping "invent"
many Christmas customs in America?*

> *Washington Irving. His SKETCH BOOK brought to
> life a "perfect" English Christmas for Americans.*

*What artist is generally credited with
creating the image of the jolly old
Santa Claus we know today?*

> *Thomas Nast, who drew the illustrations that
> accompanied the 1881 publication of Clement
> Clarke Moore's "The Night Before Christmas" in
> HARPER'S WEEKLY. Nast is considered by many as
> the father of American political cartooning, and
> he created the popular images of both the GOP
> elephant, and the Democrat's donkey.*

What did Francis P. Church's 1897 editorial assure a young reader named Virginia?

"Yes, Virginia, there is a Santa Claus." Church's editorial first appeared in the NEW YORK SUN. It ran every year thereafter until the paper closed in 1949.

Robert L. May, a copywriter at the Chicago-based Montgomery Ward department stores, created a story about what Christmas character to help boost sales in their stores?

"Rudolph the Red-Nosed Reindeer." Later a song was written by Johnny Marks, who offered it to Bing Crosby. Bing turned it down, and it was eventually recorded by Gene Autrey, becoming one of the most beloved Christmas songs of the 1940s

*What do Buddy and his cousin deliver
to the townspeople in Truman Capote's
"A Christmas Memory"?*

> *Fruitcake.*

*What famous children's author wrote
the story "The Fir Tree," about
Christmas from a tree's perspective?*

> *Hans Christian Anderson. If this story doesn't
> make you switch to artificial Christmas trees,
> nothing will.*

*Norman Rockwell's "Merrie
Christmas" series of drawings was
based on what Dickens novel?*

> THE PICKWICK PAPERS.

What J. D. Salinger novel takes place during Holden Caulfield's Christmas break in New York?

THE CATCHER IN THE RYE.

What high-energy chef lent his "bam!" to holiday cooking with a Creole twist?

Emeril Lagasse, with EMERIL'S CREOLE CHRISTMAS, published in 1997.

What do-it-yourself maven made millions of women feel guilty for not making their own wrapping paper with the 1995 book HANDMADE CHRISTMAS?

Martha Stewart.

The following Christmas books feature a favorite children's character. Can you match up the description with the title?

1) *Spot's First Christmas*
2) *Clifford's Christmas*
3) *Madeline's Christmas*
4) *Garfield's Night*
5) *Barney's Favorite Christmas Stories*
6) *Elmo's 12 Days of Christmas*
7) *Grouch's Christmas*

a) *a big red dog*
b) *a red-headed French girl*
c) *a yellow spotted dog*
d) *an orange striped cat*
e) *a green muppet with a bad attitude*
f) *a big purple dinosaur*
g) *a red muppet with a high-pitched voice*

$$1 - c;\ 2 - a;\ 3 - b;\ 4 - d;\ 5 - f;\ 6 - g;\ 7 - f$$

What famous author also penned the
LETTERS FROM FATHER CHRISTMAS—a
collection of annual illustrated letters
written from "Santa Claus"?

> J. R. R. Tolkien, author of THE HOBBIT.

Name the title of the book that
involved the tough Herdman kids
taking over their town's Christmas
pageant.

> THE BEST CHRISTMAS PAGEANT EVER, by Barbara
> Robinson.

Where did Dylan Thomas's reflections
of his boyhood Christmases take place?

> Wales (A CHILD'S CHRISTMAS IN WALES).

Chris Van Allsburg's POLAR EXPRESS *features a young boy on a mysterious train ride to where?*

> The North Pole.

What children's book is about a dog who is convinced she might be a reindeer?

> OLIVE THE OTHER REINDEER. *Olive hears the line "all of the other reindeer" from "Rudolph the Red-Nosed Reindeer," and mistakenly hears "Olive the other reindeer..."*

How many ghosts visited Ebenezer Scrooge in Charles Dickens' A CHRISTMAS CAROL?

> Four. (Jacob Marley, and the Ghosts of Christmas Past, Present, and Yet to Come.)

How long had Marley been dead at the beginning of A CHRISTMAS CAROL?

> *Seven years.*

What is the name of Scrooge's poor employee?

> *Bob Cratchit.*

What was the name of Scrooge's first employer, shown to him by the Ghost of Christmas Past?

> *Old Fezziwig.*

What color was the Ghost of Christmas Present's robe?

> *Green, lined with white fur.*

What color does the Ghost of
Christmas Yet to Come sport?

> *Black.*

What are the last five words of
Dickens' A CHRISTMAS CAROL?

> *"God bless Us, Every One!"*

MERRY
CHRISTMAS

TO:

FROM: